Good Evening

!

(insert name here)

For Those About
To Learn,
WE SALUTE YOU!

ISBN 0-9756834-0-3

Words by Paul and Barry.
Pictures by Paul.
www.paulmcneil.com

Paul would like to thank:
Barry for knowing the alphabet so well,
BT for his love of music,
Ashisha, Kathleen, Caroline, Carla,
Soph, Brett, Ann-Marie, Wayne, Jonas,
Jeremy, Amy, Jim Marshall, Derek Smalls,
Me Mum, Me family, Me mates,
the Kids (they're alright)

Barry would like to thank:
Paul for inviting me up onstage to jam
on M Is For Metal, The Fluffy Boys for two
decades of joyous ineptitude, and
rock and roll for giving me
the best years of my life.

Legals by Brett Oaten
www.brettoaten.com.au
Produced by Jeremy Gordon
Printed by the good folk of Korea

LOVE POLICE PTY LTD
8 Marlborough Street.
Surry Hills NSW 2010
Australia.
PH +61 2 96992512

For this book and other rockin stuff visit:
www.lovepolice.com.au

A portion of the profits of this book are
donated to The Royal Institute for Deaf
and Blind Children.

M is för METAL!

THE LOUDEST ALPHABET BOOK ON EARTH

 Paül McNeil and **Barrÿ Divola**

Illustrated by
Paul McNeil

To Be Read LOUD!

is for Angus
whose riffs are a hit.
He's a grown man
in a schoolboy outfit.

**is for Ballad,
a song slow and boring.
Break out the lighters
before you start snoring.**

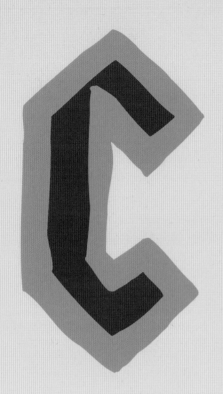

**is for Carol
who checks the guest list.
I think your name's on it
so let's stamp your wrist.**

is for Drums
that go boom-boom-boom bash,
and dubba-dubba, dubba-dubba,
dubba-dubba,
Crash!

is for Everyone stuck up the back. This next song's for you… it's called "Back in Black"

**is for Feedback,
the buzz in your ears.
Let's hope we're not deaf
in a couple of years.**

**is for Groupies
who really love bands,
and the bands love the groupies
they go hand in hand.**

is for Hair
teased with hairspray and gel,
and also for Highway
that's going to Hell.

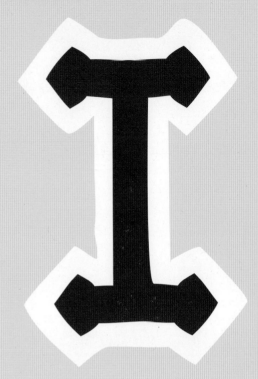

**is for Izzy and
those gorgeous curls,
but Izzy a boy or Izzy a girl?**

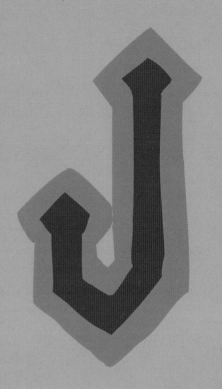

is for Jimi,
an experienced guy.
He can play with both hands,
his teeth and one eye!

is for Kiss,
with make-up that runs.
Gene is the one
with the longest of tongues.

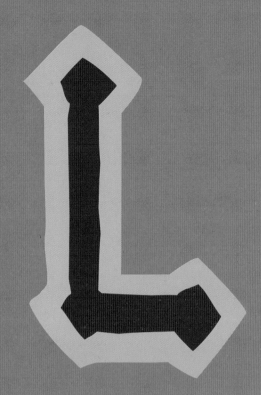

**is for Limousines,
really long cars.
Normal sized ones
just aren't for stars.**

**is for Monsters of rock
who are scary.
They're a real motley crew
who are dumb, loud and hairy.**

**is for Nigel
who can't find the stage.
Don't worry, he'll get there,
so let's turn the page.**

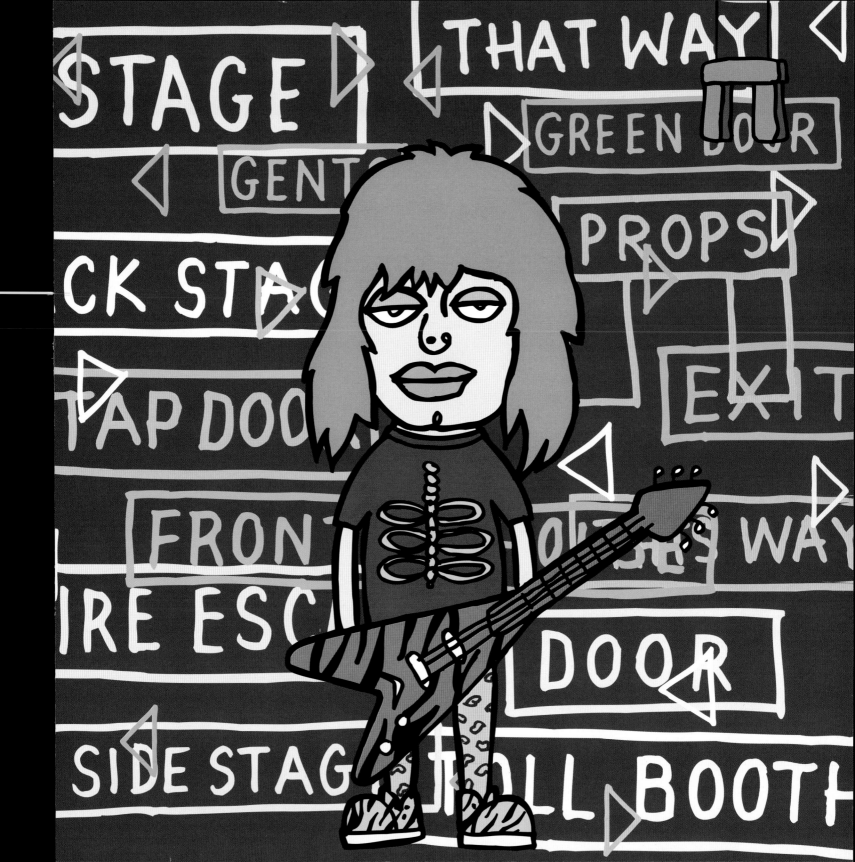

**is for Ozzy
who cleans up dog-doo.
He rests on the Sabbath
and other days too.**

is for Pop
(wait up, something's wrong!)
This book's about Metal,
not that kind of song!

is for Queen,
who were fruity as mango.
Scaramouche, Scaramouche,
can you do the fandango?

is for Roadie
who sets up the gear,
and then packs it up
and says "We're out of here."

**is for Stones
that just keep on rolling.
Most of their fans
have now switched to
Lawn Bowling.**

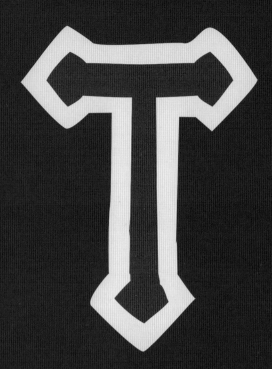

is for TV sets
thrown in the pool.
You're in for a shock
if you think this is cool.

is for Unicorns,
they don't exist,
except in Rock songs,
where they gallop through mist.

is for Volume
that's louder than hell.
What's that you're saying?
I really can't tell.

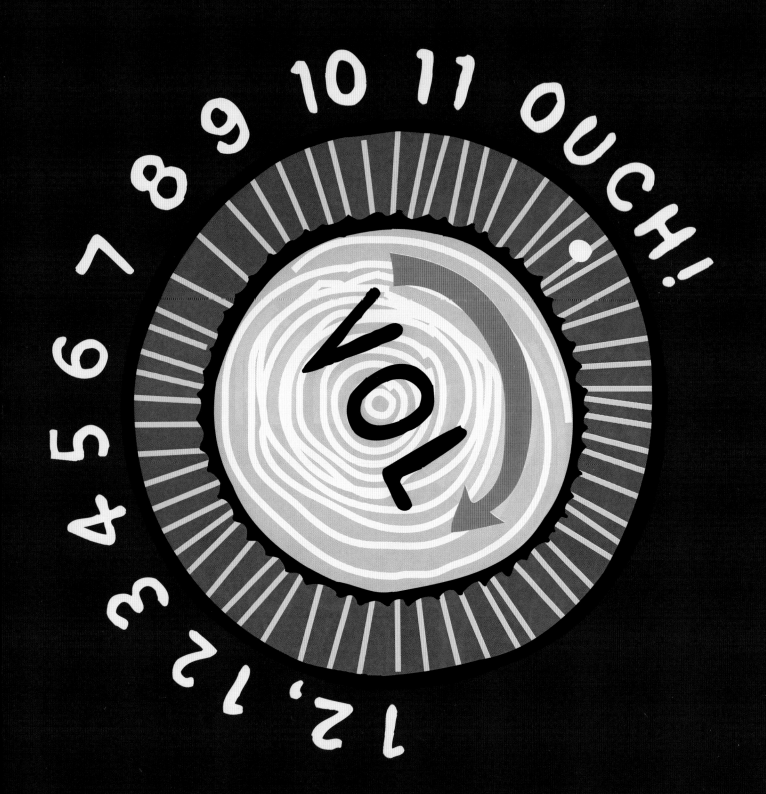

**is for Windmill,
that Pete likes to do.
But just who is Pete?
Who-who
Who-who?**

**marks the spot
where we meet to rehearse.
Is this bit the chorus,
or is it the verse?**

is for Yobbos
with mullets on top.
They yell out "Play Faster!"
You can't make them stop.

is for Zeppelin,
we followed, they led.
Stairway goes to heaven
and then off to bed.

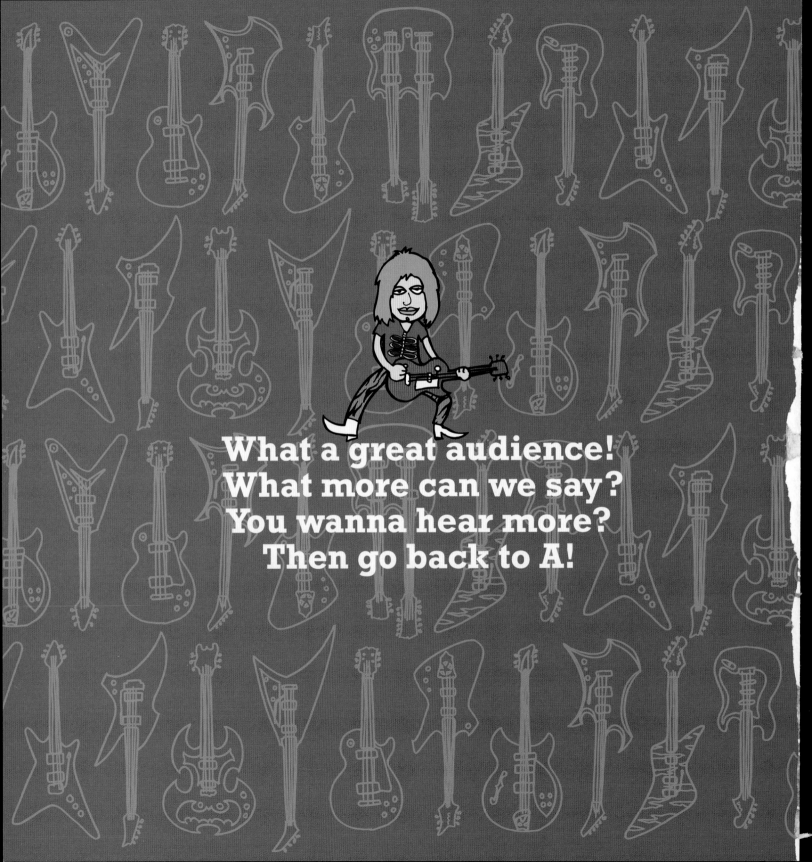